# The Piano Collection
## Thirty film themes arranged for piano solo

© 2017 by Faber Music Ltd
First published by Faber Music Ltd in 2017
Bloomsbury House
74–77 Great Russell Street
London WC1B 3DA
Cover designed by Chloë Alexander Design
Printed in England by Caligraving Ltd
All rights reserved

This paper is 100% recyclable

ISBN: 0-571-53968-8
EAN: 978-0-571-53968-0

To buy Faber Music publications or to find out about the full range of titles available
please contact your local music retailer or Faber Music sales enquiries:

Faber Music Limited, Burnt Mill, Elizabeth Way, Harlow CM20 2HX
Tel: +44 (0)1279 82 89 82   Fax: +44 (0)1279 82 89 83
sales@fabermusic.com   fabermusicstore.com

# Alone in Kyoto

### (from *Lost in Translation*)

Music by Jean-Benoît Dunckel and Nicolas Godin

Freely

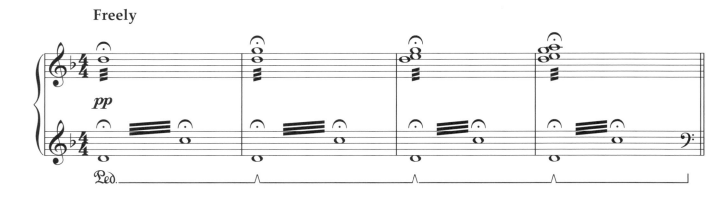

(Small notes 2° only)

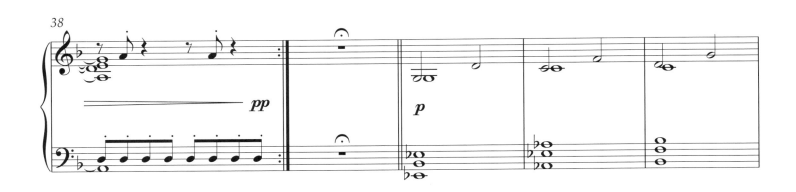

(Small notes optional)

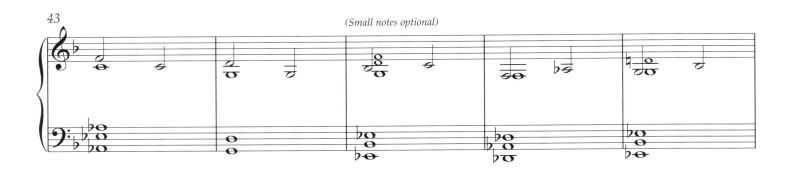

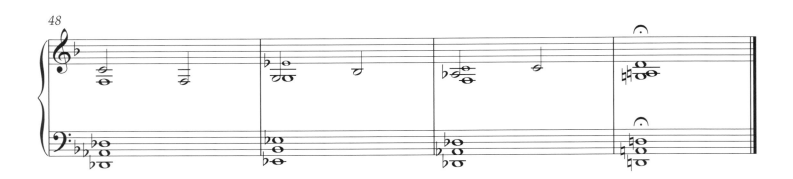

# Bella's Lullaby

### (from *Twilight*)

Music by Carter Burwell

Moderately

# The Cider House Rules (Main Title)

Music by Rachel Portman

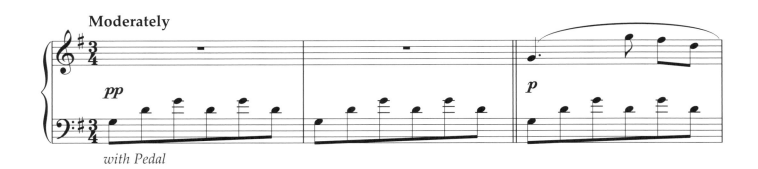

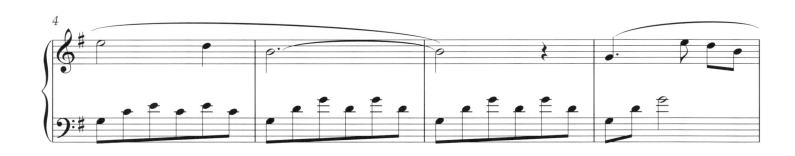

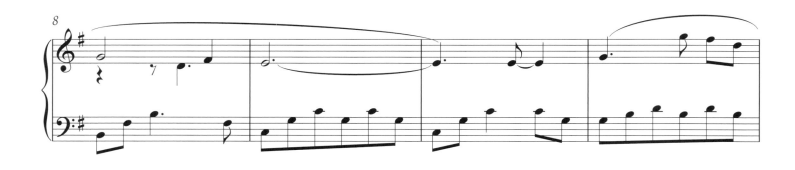

# Cruella De Vil

## (from *101 Dalmatians*)

Words and Music by Mel Leven

# Elevator Song

## (from *X&Y*)

### Music by Keaton Henson

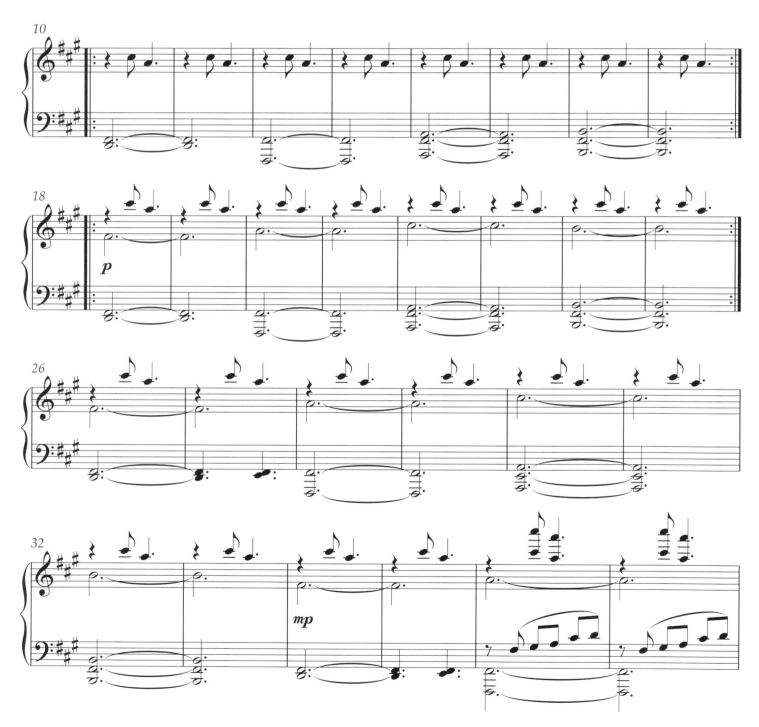

# Forrest Gump

**Music by Alan Silvestri**

# Gone With The Wind

Music by Max Steiner

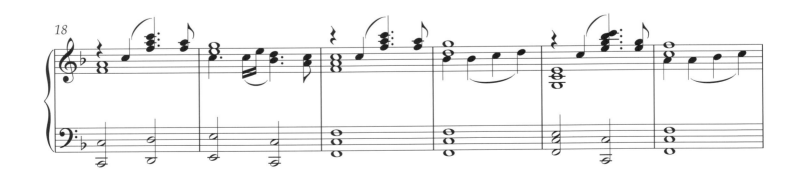

# Chocolat

Music by Rachel Portman

Slowly, expressively

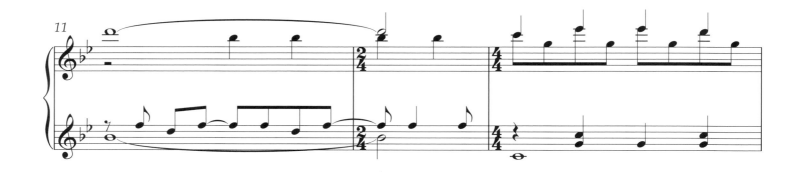

rit.     a tempo

Moderately, in 2

# Harry's Wondrous World

## (from *Harry Potter and the Philosopher's Stone*)

Music by John Williams

# The Hanging Tree

## (from *The Hunger Games: Mockingjay Part 1*)

Words and Music by Suzanne Collins, Jeremy Fraites and Wesley Schultz

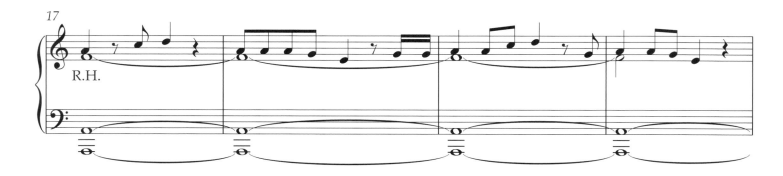

# Heal

## (from *If I Stay*)

Words and Music by Tom Odell

# I Wanna Be Like You

## (from *The Jungle Book*)

Words and Music by Richard M. Sherman and Robert B. Sherman

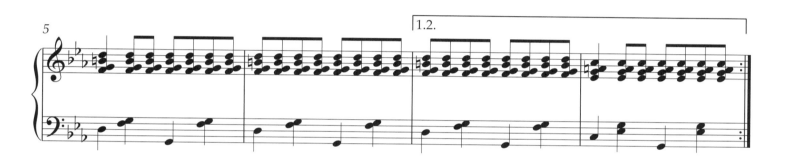

# In Noctem

### (from *Harry Potter and the Half-Blood Prince*)

Words and Music by Nicholas Hooper

# Let It Go

## (from *Frozen*)

Words and Music by Robert Lopez and Kristen Anderson-Lopez

Mysteriously

with Pedal

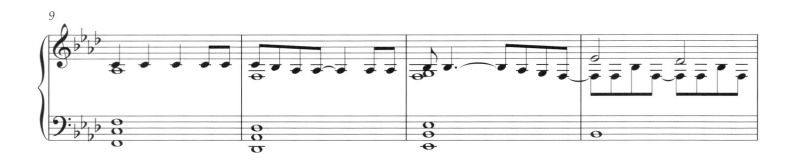

**Broadly**

# Long Way Down

## (from *The Fault in Our Stars*)

### Words and Music by Tom Odell

To Coda ⊕

D.𝄋 al Coda

# Love Me Like You Do

## (from *50 Shades of Grey*)

Words and Music by Max Martin, Savan Kotecha,
Ilya Salmanzadeh, Ali Payami and Tove Ebba Elsa Nilsson

# Love Theme

## (from *Romeo & Juliet*)

**Music by Nino Rota**

Slowly and freely

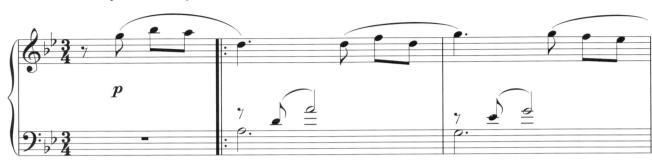

# Maybe

## (from *Annie*)

Words by Martin Charnin
Music by Charles Strouse

**Slower**

# Mia & Sebastian's Theme

## (from *La La Land*)

Music by Justin Hurwitz

Moderately slow, expressively

*Pedal ad lib. throughout*

74

# Morning Passages

(from *The Hours*)

Music by Philip Glass

# Neverland - Minor Piano Variation

## (from *Finding Neverland*)

### Music by Jan A.P. Kaczmarek

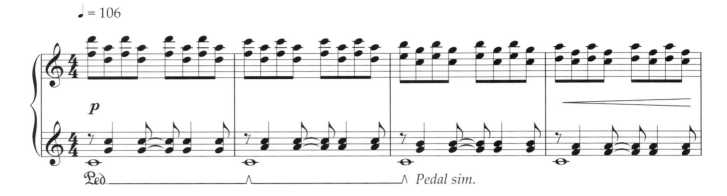

# Not About Angels

## (from *The Fault in Our Stars*)

Words and Music by Jasmine van den Bogaerde

# Not Goin' Home Anymore

## (from *Butch Cassidy and the Sundance Kid*)

Music by Burt Bacharach

♩ = 82  **Freely**

# Obliviate

## (from *Harry Potter and the Deathly Hallows Part 1*)

Music by Alexandre Desplat

Moderately slow ♩ = 76

# Prelude in E Minor (Op.28, No.4)

## (from *The Pianist*)

### Music by Frederic Chopin

# Rachel's Song
## (from *Blade Runner*)

Music by Vangelis

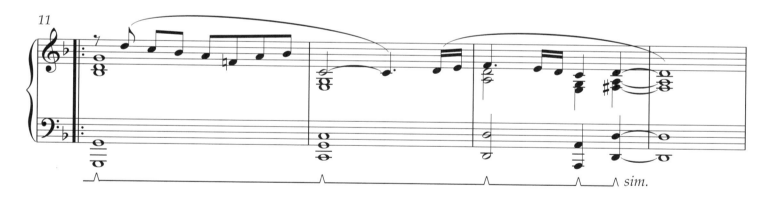

# Rey's Theme

## (from *Star Wars: The Force Awakens*)

### Music by John Williams

# See You Again

## (from *Fast and the Furious*)

Words and Music by Justin Scott Franks, Cameron Thomaz, Charlie Puth and Andrew Cedar

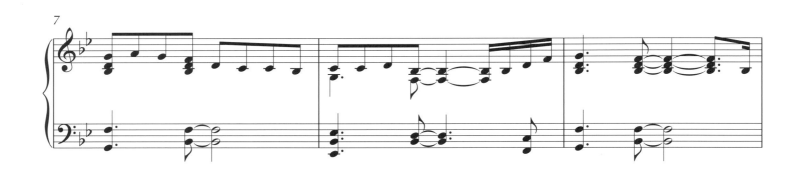

# This Is Berk

## (from *How to Train Your Dragon*)

### Music by John Powell

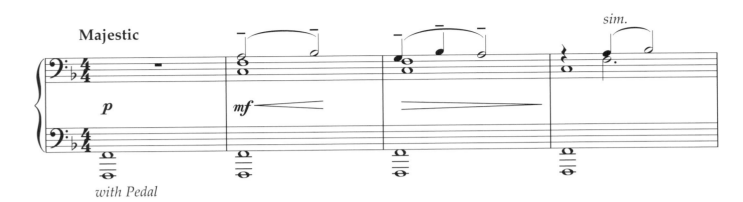

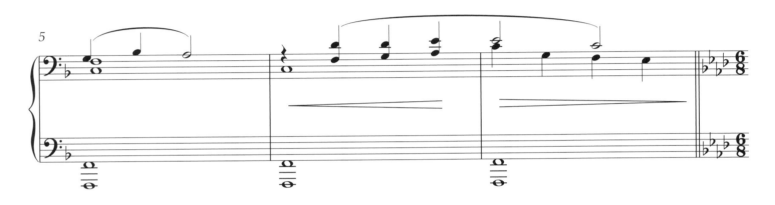

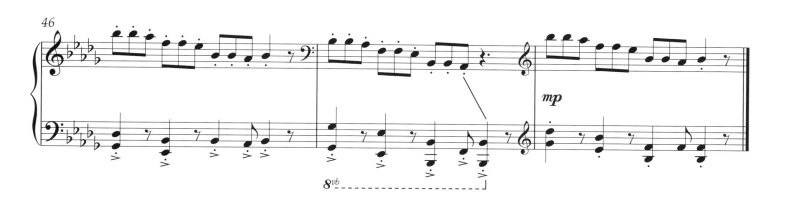

# Theme

## (from *Eternal Sunshine of the Spotless Mind*)

Music by Jon Brion